5 Worlds

BOOK 1

THE SAND WARRIOR

Mark
SIEGEL

Alexis
SIEGEL

**Xanthe
BOUMA**

**Boya
SUN**

**Matt
ROCKEFELLER**

SCHOLASTIC INC.

"One by one the five great Beacons
went dark and the Gods were gone.
And none would ever again light the
shining Beacons, save a Warrior of
Sand, crowned with living fire. . . ."
            —FROM THE HOURS OF PRINCE FELID

THE *SAND CASTLE*

EVE OF *BEACON DAY*

ISN'T THAT THE *LEE* GIRL?

YES, SHE LOOKS A LOT LIKE HER SISTER.

LET'S NOT SPEAK OF *THAT* ONE.

ESPECIALLY NOT BEFORE THE COUNCIL MEETING.

HEY, OONA!

HI, *VEA*. WOULD YOU SKIP *BEACON DAY* IF IT MEANT--

SKIP BEACON *DAY??* ARE YOU *CRAZY??*

...SAY, DID YOU PRACTICE THE *SUMMONING DANCE?*

I'M NOT CUT OUT FOR *SAND,* VEA. MY SISTER WAS THE ONE--

JUST BECAUSE *SHE RAN AWAY* DOESN'T MEAN YOU SHOULD GIVE UP! WE HAVE A FEW MINUTES. LET'S DO IT *TOGETHER!*

LET YOUR **SANDSTONE** UNWIND....

GOOD!

NOW KEEP THE **ANIFORM** CLOSE AS IT BUILDS POWER! DON'T LET IT GO....

REMEMBER...
CONTROL,
CONTROL!

UH... *OONA...?*
CONTROL...?

SHHPOOF!!!

OH WELL, *THAT* WAS PRETTY CLOSE!

HA HA!

HA HA!!

PRETTY CLOSE TO ANOTHER DISASTER!

THEY'RE ALMOST DONE SETTING UP FOR TOMORROW.

HOW COME WE STILL DON'T KNOW WHO *THE CHOSEN ONE* IS?

THIS TIME IT'S A *SECRET.* MAYBE THEY WANT TO AVOID, YOU KNOW...LIKE *LAST TIME...?*

SHUT UP, GEN.

MAYBE THE CHOSEN ONE IS *YOU,* OONA!

HAHA!

HRMPF. SO...WHERE'S *PROFESSOR PLUMB?*

DEAN PLUMB IS SPEAKING BEFORE THE *HIGH COUNCIL OF THE FIVE WORLDS!* SO I WILL CONDUCT *SUMMONING CLASS* IN HIS ABSENCE.

OH, GREAT. *KLAANTH* HATES ME.

QUIET, *SAND DANCERS!*

NOW, LET'S BEGIN WITH BASICS.

GEOMETRICS!

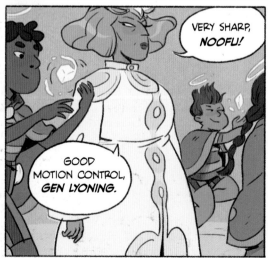

VERY SHARP, *NOOFU!*

GOOD MOTION CONTROL, *GEN LYONING.*

MISS LEE, *MISS LEE.* EVEN MORE DISTRACTED THAN USUAL. THAT'S NOT AN *ANIFORM*—THAT'S A *RUNNY MUDPIE!*

DEAN PLUMB GOES *TOO EASY* ON YOU, THAT'S OBVIOUS. LIKE HE DID WITH *YOUR SISTER.*

WHSSHH— THMP!!

?!

OOPS.

14

AHA! GOTCHA!

WE ARE ON THE VERGE OF EXTINCTION!

THE FIVE WORLDS ARE OVERHEATING!

THE OASIS OF IDYLLIA ON MOON YATTA IS NOW DESERT!

THIS IS ALL THAT REMAINS OF THE PTUHULI BIRDS ON SALASSANDRA...!

ON GRIMBO (E), THE HEAT HAS ENRAGED THE OCEAN MOSS!!

THERE ARE **WATER RIOTS** ON **TOKI** AS WE SPEAK!

THE **PLANT PEOPLE ARE DYING!**

I BELIEVE THE **ANCIENT BEACONS** ARE AT THE ROOT OF THIS OVERHEATING. **LIGHTING** THEM IS LONG OVERDUE!

THAT'S JUST A **THEORY!**

YOU SAND DANCERS AND YOUR ANCIENT **STORIES** AGAIN!

IT'S NOT **JUST** WE SAND DANCERS ANYMORE! THIS WAS CONFIRMED BY THE RESEARCH OF **PROFESSOR ETTO** HIMSELF!

THE **FLYING FORTRESS ACADEMY** WILL NEVER GRANT **THE SAND CASTLE** ACCESS TO OUR BLUE BEACON!

THE TIME FOR **YOURS AND MINE IS OVER!** OUR **LIVES** HANG IN THE BALANCE!! **COMING TOGETHER IS OUR ONLY HOPE!**

WE ALSO BELIEVE LIGHTING THE BEACONS IS THE LAST HOPE OF THE **FIVE WORLDS!**

OH SURE, SO MON DOMANI CAN **TAKE OVER** ALL ITS FORMER COLONIES AGAIN!

DOMA ELITE

REGARDLESS, DELEGATE PLUMB, YOUR **SAND DANCERS** HAVE YET TO SHOW THEY **CAN** LIGHT A BEACON. IT'S **NEVER** BEEN DONE, AND PERHAPS **NEVER SHOULD BE!**

BESIDES, **NO ONE KNOWS** WHAT HAPPENS IF WE MANAGE TO LIGHT THEM!

CONVENIENT CRISIS FOR A **POWER GRAB!**

ENOUGH ABOUT GODS

LIGHT **YOUR OWN** BEACON IF YOU CAN, BUT **STAY AWAY FROM OURS!**

ON DOMANI HEGEMONY IS OVER AND DONE WITH

AND HOW WELL DID YOUR **BEACON DAY** GO LAST TIME? I BELIEVE YOUR LAST "**CHOSEN ONE**" JUST **RAN AWAY**, DID SHE NOT?

EEEEK!!!

SWWOOP

HOW DARE YOU?! YOU **YATTANS** AND **TOKIS** KNOW NOTHING OF REAL **SAND DANCING**! THAT **FLYING FORTRESS** ISN'T EVEN A REAL SCHOOL!

AND YOUR **SAND CASTLE** IS A RELIC!

BONK!!   THMP!!   BUMP!!

WHAT IS THIS *INSULT?* SOME *SAND DANCER'S* IDEA OF A *JOKE,* PLUMB??

HAHA HAHA HAHA!!

HE HEHE HEHE HE!!

BY THE QUEEN'S MISSING ARM, WHO WOULD DARE?

I'M AFRAID WE CAN'T AGREE ON YOUR SUGGESTION, PLUMB.

WE JUST NEED MORE EVIDENCE ABOUT THE BURN

BESIDES, ISN'T THERE A STARBALL GAME RIGHT ON THAT DAY?

...THROWN IN *PRISON*...

...*MAJOR* DIPLOMATIC INCIDENT...

TODAY YOU ARE GETTING YOUR FIRST *SANDSTONE,* MY LITTLE MOONS!

WAAAH! THE SAND'S IN MY EYES!!!

READY? *LIFELIKE ANIFORMS,* PLEASE. AND WHERE IS MISS LEE *THIS TIME?*

OOF!

WHUMF!!

NO ONE IS ALLOWED ON THE ROOFTOPS!

THEN WHY ARE YOU HERE?

NICE SAND MASK! WHO ARE YOU?

VECTOR SANDERSON. WHO ARE YOU?

OONA LEE.

YOU'RE NOT FROM THE SAND CASTLE.... WHY ARE YOU MASKED?

...

NO ONE'S SUPPOSED TO KNOW **WHO I AM.**

YOU'RE PLUMB'S **CHOSEN ONE,** AREN'T YOU?

I JUST **HEARD** HIM IN THE HIGH COUNCIL!

THINGS ARE **SO BAD!** WORSE THAN I EVER KNEW! IDYLLIA...**THE PLANT PEOPLE...**

THE **GROWN-UPS** IN THERE, ALL THOSE OFFICIALS... THEY'RE **USELESS!**

THEY WERE JUST BICKERING AND **MOCKING** PLUMB! WHILE THE WORLDS ARE **BURNING UP** FROM THE INSIDE!

WELL, ABOUT BEACON DAY...

...I CAN'T COMBINE SANDS! IT JUST DOESN'T WORK.

COMBINE SANDS?!

DEAN PLUMB WANTS ME TO COMBINE SANDS. BUT I KEEP DISAPPOINTING HIM!

I KNOW THE FEELING.

MY SANDFORMS ALWAYS GET AWAY FROM ME.

YIKES!!

SSFFFF

WHOA!
THEY'RE...

SORRY! I
DIDN'T MEAN
TO--

NO, LOOK!
THEY ARE
COMBINING!

THIS IS WHAT
PLUMB WAS
TALKING
ABOUT....

WHY? WHAT'S
THAT SUPPOSED
TO DO?

I DON'T KNOW!
PLUMB BELIEVES
THAT'S *THE KEY* TO
LIGHTING THE
BEACONS.

IT'S NOT *HOLDING.*

IF ONLY *JESSA* WERE HERE...

IN HER FIFTH TERM, SHE WAS PRODUCING ANIFORMS MOST *TEACHERS* COULDN'T MAKE. *SHE* COULD HAVE HELPED YOU.

LEE?! *THAT* LEE?! YOUR SISTER IS *JESSA LEE?*

YES.

JESSA LEE IS THE *GREATEST SAND DANCER* EVER! IF *ANYONE* CAN LIGHT A BEACON, IT'S *HER!*

IF SHE ONLY KNEW WHAT WAS *AT STAKE,* MAYBE...

SO...DID SHE REALLY GO *MAD?*

THAT'S WHAT EVERYONE *SAYS.*

THIS IS *SO* STRANGE.... *TODAY* SHE WROTE TO ME FOR THE *FIRST* TIME IN YEARS.

SHE DID?! WHAT DID SHE SAY?!

DOESN'T MAKE SENSE...

"TRUST ME, OONA, *NOW IF EVER!* TAKE THIS SHIP TO *MOON YATTA.* I PROMISE I WILL EXPLAIN EVERYTHING! SISTERS ARE FOREVER. LOVE, *JESSA.*"

AND SHE GAVE YOU A *TICKET.*

THE *MOON MOTH! TOMORROW* MORNING. ON *BEACON DAY?!*

I CAN'T *MISS* BEACON DAY!! WHEN IT'S FINALLY GOING TO BE *LIT!*

IT'S *NOT.*

IT'S HOPELESS.

DON'T **SAY** THAT!

SOMEONE HAS TO LIGHT IT. IT'S THE ONLY HOPE FOR ALL THE WORLDS!

I TELL YOU I **CAN'T!** NOT ALONE!

. . .

HM. I WONDER... HAVE YOU BEEN DOWN TO THE **SAND MUSEUM** YET?

NO.

IT'S DOWN NEAR THE **QUEEN'S BONES.** THERE'S A LOT OF STUFF THERE. ABOUT SANDS. MAYBE EVEN ABOUT **COMBINING** THEM. LET ME SHOW YOU! BUT **FIRST**...

WHAT...?

I HAVE TO SEE YOUR FACE!

HUH?! BY THE QUEEN'S WHISKERS! YOU...YOU'RE A *TOKI*??

AND? YOU NEVER MET ONE BEFORE?

WELL, THE SERVANTS...! SO--THAT *DARK SAND* IS *TOKI* SAND?! WERE YOU TRAINED AT THAT *OTHER* SCHOOL?

FLYING FORTRESS ACADEMY! FROM THE TIME I WAS A BABY.

BUT... BUT I THOUGHT THE *SAND CASTLE* AND THE *FLYING FORTRESS* *HATED* EACH OTHER!

PLUMB VISITED WITH DOMANI DIPLOMATS, BUT *HE WAS SECRETLY TEACHING ME.* I CAME TO UNDERSTAND THERE IS *SOMETHING ROTTEN* IN THE HEART OF THE FORTRESS THESE DAYS!

TOKI STANDS *AGAINST* LIGHTING THE BEACONS! I ESCAPED TO CONTINUE MY TRAINING BECAUSE *I BELIEVE LIGHTING THEM IS THE RIGHT THING TO DO.*

OKAY. FOLLOW ME, **VECTOR SANDERSON.**

I CAN'T CONTROL MY SAND. BESIDES, THERE'S **NO CHANCE** PLUMB WOULD ALLOW THAT.

IT TURNS OUT MY SISTER HAD ALL THE **TALENT.**

MAYBE **YOU** SHOULD **SAND DANCE** WITH ME TOMORROW.

THUMP!

YOUR SISTER NEVER TOLD YOU **WHY SHE RAN AWAY** ON BEACON DAY?

NOT REALLY. NO.

WHAT IF YOU WENT TO **GET HER** AND BROUGHT HER BACK HERE? **TO HELP ME?**

THE CEREMONY IS TOMORROW! THERE'S **NO TIME!** EVEN IF I **COULD** PERSUADE HER.

HHHSSS

MAYBE THERE'S SOME **CLUE!** LOOK OVER HERE... **"THE SANDS OF THE WORLDS"**...ONE OF EACH!

EVEN THE EMERALD SAND OF **GRIMBO (E)!**

FROM EVERY WORLD **EXCEPT** TOKI.

WELL... YEAH.

LOOK! *"THE SAND WARRIOR"*!

AND THIS ONE... *"THE KEY"*...

I WONDER IF I COULD....

NICELY DONE, FOR THE SISTER *WITHOUT ANY TALENT!*

UH-OH.

SSSHLOOP!

CAN'T YOU STOP IT?

NO!!

THERE! IT'S *STOPPING!* SUMMON IT BACK INTO YOUR *SANDSTONE!*

WHY DID IT STOP *HERE?*

OH, *THAT!* I'M NOT SURE *ANYONE* COULD DECIPHER THESE RUNES!

I *CAN!* IT'S AN ANCIENT *FELID SCRIPT....* IT SAYS... "THE SAND WARRIOR HAS *FIVE DOMANI DAYS...*

...TO LIGHT THE FIRST BEACON WITH... *LIVING FIRE.*"

IT SAYS FIVE DOMANI DAYS?!

THEN THERE'S STUFF ABOUT...*THE THREE SUNS* ALIGNING... UP UNTIL--

VECTOR! IT'S NOT TOO LATE!!

HUH? YOU MEAN *EVEN IF* THE CEREMONY *FAILS* TOMORROW...YOU WOULD *STILL* HAVE TIME...

...*TO FIND JESSA* AND BRING HER BACK BEFORE IT'S TOO *LATE!*

AND TOGETHER WITH HER *YOU CAN LIGHT THE BEACON!*

BUT I NEED TO *LEAVE* RIGHT AWAY....

YOU CAN'T JUST *WALK* OUT OF HERE, CAN YOU?

THE GIRLS WOULD *RAT* ME OUT.

BUT... TOMORROW MORNING...

YES! EVERYONE WILL BE *DISTRACTED* WITH THE CEREMONY!

OONA, *YOU* MUST BRING BACK JESSA LEE.

WELCOME TO THE *177TH BEACON DAY* CEREMONY, HELD ON THE ALIGNMENT OF *THE THREE SUNS*, EVERY SEVEN YEARS--

COMBINING *MASTERY* OF THE SAND DANCING ARTS WITH THE *INNOCENCE* OF YOUTH, THE CHOSEN ONE INVITES *THE LIVING FIRE*...

...AND ON YOUR RIGHT, THESE *FELID* CARVINGS SHOW THE CREATION OF THE FIVE ANCIENT BEACONS...*THE QUEEN* AND HER ARCHITECT... THE QUEEN'S *SACRIFICE*...

...*WATCH* YOUR STEP HERE! THIS WAY TO *THE SAND MUSEUM*, WHERE THE GREAT QUEEN'S *BONES* ARE LAID TO REST. THANKS TO THEM, THE SAND CASTLE HAS *HELD ITS FORM* FOR GENERATIONS!

AW, MOM, IT'S TIME! ALL MY FRIENDS ARE AT THE *STARBALL* GAME!

CHAWLEY, ANY MORE WHINING AND *I SWEAR*...

WHOOSH!

OOPS, DIDN'T CLOSE THE HATCH PROPERLY. BETTER GO DO THAT!

H2O

CONCENTRATE

STOP!

ATTENTION, ALL UNITS...

DID HE GET *ALL* THREE?

YEP! *ARNALDS, TWYPSEN,* AAAND...*LETOKO!*

CONGRATULATIONS! YOU WIN TWO TICKETS TO TONIGHT'S GAME!

WOO-HOO! WE'RE OFF TO SEE *JAX AMBOY!*

NOSEBLEED SECTION, BUT STILL...THAT WEIRD KID DELIVERED!

AAAH, THAT'S BETTER!

THANK THE GODS FOR THE UN-CONTAMINATED *OFF-WORLD* STUFF.

BLESS YOU, YOUNG *AN TZU.* YOU'RE A GODS-SEND. YOUR MOM AND DAD WOULD BE *SO PROUD* OF YOU.

I JUST WISH IT WAS *DECENT* FOOD, MRS. LESTAK.

WELL, IT'S NOT OUR LOT TO BE *FUSSY LIKE A SAND DANCER,* IS IT?

AH!

...GETTING...

...WORSE...

CAN'T BELIEVE THEY'RE STILL USING OLD-FUEL *SHOEBOXES!*

AND *STINKING UP* OUR SKIES WITH THEM, TOO!

YEAH, LIKE THEIR *FLAG*, THE SMELLY *ARMPIT OF TOKI!* **HAHAHAHAHAHA!**

THAT'S NOT FUNNY.

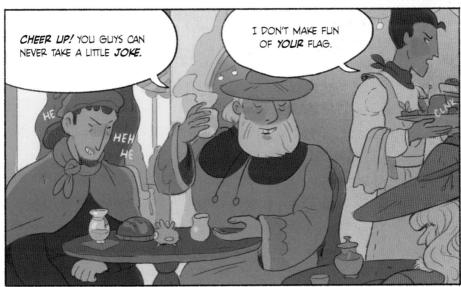

CHEER UP! YOU GUYS CAN NEVER TAKE A LITTLE *JOKE.*

I DON'T MAKE FUN OF *YOUR* FLAG.

COMMANDER ZAYD...

WE'RE READY FOR *THE INVASION*...

...BUT IT IS GOING TO BE HARDER TO MANAGE *THE OCCUPATION.*

ARE YOU SURE ABOUT *THE SAND CASTLE?* THE OTHER WORLDS WILL SEE THAT AS *A STEP TOO FAR....*

THE OTHER WORLDS *WON'T* GET INVOLVED, *GENERAL RONAK. OUR PRINCE* HAS SEEN TO THAT ALREADY.

HE HASN'T FORGOTTEN THE *INSULT* OF *THE FIVE WORLDS WAR,* AND NEITHER SHOULD WE!

TOKI'S HUMILIATION ENDS TODAY.

I CAN *NEVER* FORGET THE WAR, COMMANDER *ZAYD*. I FOUGHT IN IT BEFORE YOU WERE BORN. BUT YOUR *TACTICS* WORRY ME. THE *BONES* ESPECIALLY--

OUR *COBALT PRINCE* WAS CLEAR. THE *SACRED BONES* WILL BE GIVEN A BETTER HOME AT *THE FLYING FORTRESS*.

AND WHATEVER IT TAKES, THE BEACON *CANNOT, MUST NOT, WILL NOT BE LIT*.

THIS IS *MORE* THAN A WAR ON *MON DOMANI*, GENERAL RONAK.

THIS IS *THE MIMIC ITSELF* WE ARE FIGHTING, NO LESS! IT HAS HAD *THE SAND CASTLE* UNDER ITS *EVIL INFLUENCE* FOR TOO LONG. NOW PREPARE *PHASE ONE*.

YES, COMMANDER.

MEANWHILE, IN THE STREETS OF *CHRYSALIS*

BLESS YOU, GIRL. YOU'RE VERY KIND.

STARBALL STADIUM

JUMP

YEAH!!
YEAH!

...AND THE PERIDOT PIRATES ARE OFF!

THE *AMBER LEATHERHEADS'* OPENING GAMBIT IS A *POWERFUL* CHARGE, BUT CAN THEY BEAT *THE MAGNET*?

WHOOO!

GO!!

OH NO!! *JERROL WILKIN* JUST GOT *SUCKED BACK* THREE PACES, BUT HE'S FIGHTING BACK!!

ZZZT!

SLAM!

WHOO! LEATHERHEADS!!

HEADING FOR A *COLLISION* WITH THE PIRATES' FRONT LINE!! *A RED FLAG!!!*

CRK

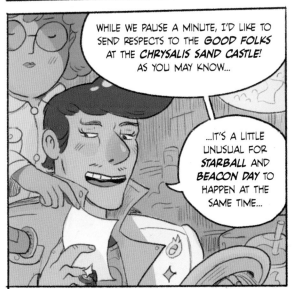

WHILE WE PAUSE A MINUTE, I'D LIKE TO SEND RESPECTS TO THE *GOOD FOLKS* AT THE *CHRYSALIS SAND CASTLE!* AS YOU MAY KNOW...

...IT'S A LITTLE UNUSUAL FOR *STARBALL* AND *BEACON DAY* TO HAPPEN AT THE SAME TIME...

SO LET'S SEND OUR VERY **BEST WISHES** TO THIS YEAR'S **CHOSEN ONE!**

CLP CLAP

CLP CLAP

BUT IF--LIKE **THE LAST CHOSEN ONE**--HE DECIDES HE HAS **BETTER THINGS** TO DO TODAY, WE'LL GLADLY WELCOME HIM HERE FOR **A GREAT GAME OF STARBALL!!**

AAHAHAHH HA HA

HAHA!

HA HA

HA HA

HA

GOODBYE, **CHRYSALIS!**

THE WORLDS ARE WORTH SAVING, **JESSA...**

ZOOOOM

...COME BACK WITH ME!

...JAX AMBOY!!!!

YEAA AAAH DS

JAX!

JAX!!

JAX!!

LADIES AND GENTLEMEN, FOR THOSE OF YOU WHO CAN TEAR YOUR EYES AWAY FROM *THE STARBALL GAME* FOR A MOMENT...

ZOOOM

...ON THE LEFT WE NOW HAVE A BEAUTIFUL VIEW OF DOWNTOWN *CHRYSALIS*...

...AND ON YOUR RIGHT THE *RED GRID RELAY* TOWER, WHICH BRINGS CLEAN ENERGY TO ALL OF *MON DOMANI!*

>BIP<

>BIP<

IN FACT, IT POWERS *THIS VERY SHIP!*

WHA...?

WHAT HAPPENED?

THE...THE *RED RELAY* JUST... *EXPLODED*...! NEW SHIPS WERE ALL FALLING...AND I WAS *IN ONE!*

CARETAKER GODS! I HOPE MY FRIENDS ARE SAFE.

ME TOO!

SAND DANCER GIRL! OVER HERE!

MR. AMBOY? MR. AMBOY?!

IT'S JAX AMBOY!!

I'M AFRAID I CAN'T *MOVE*. DO YOU THINK YOU COULD GET THESE THINGS OFF ME?

HE'S ALIVE!!

WHAT JUST HAPPENED?

THE RED GRID *BLEW UP*....

UNGH! SHIPS FELL OUT OF THE SKY!

WE DON'T *KNOW* WHAT'S HAPPENING.

WHY ARE *YOU TWO* STILL INTACT?

CREEAK

I SHOULD'VE *DIED.* BUT THEN I SAW *HER*--

SHE'S ONE OF THOSE *SAND DANCERS*.... SHE JUST *APPEARED* IN THE MIDDLE OF THIS *SAND THING* AND IT SAVED ME. *IT SAVED US BOTH!*

WAS IT A *SAND WARRIOR?*

WHAT'S A *SAND WARRIOR?*

NO, OF COURSE IT WASN'T!

HERE, HELP ME LIFT THIS.

MY *UNCLE JEP* WOULD FIND THAT VERY INTERESTING.

NGH!

TOO HEAVY!!

WHAT'S THAT?

IT'S CALLED A *SANDSTONE.*

CAN IT HELP?

MAYBE.

WHOA.

MY ARM!

GAH!

D-DON'T WORRY, **MR. AMBOY.** WE'LL... WE'LL GET YOU OUT OF HERE. **WE'LL GET HELP.**

CAN YOU WALK?

I THINK SO.

OH NO, NO, NO, NO, NO...

HE SHOULD BE BLEEDING! MAYBE THE HEAT **CAUTERIZED** HIS WOUND?

HE'S **SO** AMAZING.

THERE!!

...THERE *ARE* NO SHIPS TO BOARD, I TELL YOU!

WHAT HAPPENED? WAS IT AN ACCIDENT?

NO, IT WAS *NO ACCIDENT!!*

EVERY RED GRID RELAY ON THE PLANET EXPLODED AT THE *SAME* TIME. *IT'S AN ATTACK!*

BUT *WHO* IS ATTACKING US?

COMMS CUT OUT BEFORE THEY COULD SAY.

HAVE YOU SEEN MY FATHER? WIDE-BRIM HAT, *SALASSI* GOLD ON HIS EARS?

I NEED TO CALL HOME. I NEED TO CALL HOME. I NEED TO--

DEVICES ALL *DEAD.* NO COMMUNICATIONS! *PLEASE* MOVE AWAY FROM THE WRECKAGE!

NOT **ALL** THE SHIPS CAME DOWN.

THOSE ARE **TOKI** TRASH BARGES.

OLD-FUEL SHOEBOXES. THEY WEREN'T POWERED BY THE RED GRID.

BUT WHY ARE THEY JUST **STAYING UP THERE?** CAN'T THEY **HELP?**

MAYBE **THE TOKI** ARE ATTACKING **MON DOMANI?** COULD THAT BE? LET'S HEAD TO **VICTORY PLAZA.** WE SHOULD FIND YOU SOME HELP THERE, **JAX AMBOY.**

THE FALL OF THE SAND CASTLE

COMMANDER *ZAYD,* PHASE ONE IS COMPLETE.

WITHOUT THE *RED GRID RELAY...*

SHG SHG

SHG SH

...*MON DOMANI* HAS NO AIR FORCE OR MAJOR TRANSPORTS.

GOOD. INITIATE PHASE TWO. HEAD TO *THE SAND CASTLE.*

THEY'RE IN FOR A *SURPRISE.*

94

IS *HE* DOING THAT?

WHAT ARE THOSE...?

?!?!

GAH!!

NO!!

NO!!!

VECTOR!!!

IS *HE* DOING THAT?

WHAT ARE THOSE...?

?!?!

GAH!!

NO!!

NO!!!

VECTOR!!!

NO! NOT THE CHOSEN ONE!!

KRAAK!

CRASH!

MAKE ANIFORMS AROUND THE QUEEN!

KRAK

FREEZE!!!

THOSE THINGS?!

THEY'RE... HEATING UP!

101

VEA! VECTOR! THIS WAY!

CRAK

OONA! THEY TOOK THE QUEEN!! GET AWAY!! FIND YOUR SISTER!

HISSH-TSSHH

OONA! YOU'RE THE LAST HOPE! THE LAST OF THE THREE--

?!

AAH!

THEY'RE TAKING THEM AWAY!!

THESE BOTS
DON'T EVEN KNOW
WHAT HAPPENED...

Chapter 5
PASSAGE TO MAYADOLIS

THEY DESTROYED THE SAND CASTLE! BUT WHY?

THE TOKI DON'T WANT THE BEACON TO BE LIT!

AND VEA...

...THEY CAPTURED *THE CHOSEN ONE* AND ALL THE SAND DANCERS!

ALL THE SAND DANCERS, EXCEPT *ONE*.

WHERE WILL *YOU* GO NOW?

111

I...I STILL HAVE TO GET TO *MOON YATTA*. NOW MORE THAN EVER. I NEED TO FIND *MY SISTER*.

WHAT ABOUT YOU, *MR. AMBOY*?

YOU HAVE TO GET YOUR ARM TAKEN CARE OF!

ONLY MY *UNCLE JEP* CAN HELP ME. AND HE LIVES ALL THE WAY IN *MAYAPOLIS CITY*.

I KNOW SOMEONE WHO CAN GET YOU TO *MAYAPOLIS!* THIS WAY! A *DRAINAGE TUNNEL* LEADS TO MY HOMETOWN, *SAO SABLO*.

DID YOU SAY *MAYAPOLIS?*

THAT'S WHERE THE *MOON MOTH* IS.

IT'S AN *OLD-FUEL SHIP*, SO THERE'S STILL A CHANCE IT'S RUNNING....

I'M COMING WITH YOU!

HERE, LET ME HELP YOU UP, *MR. AMBOY!*

HNG

YOU CAN CALL ME *JAX.* EVERYBODY DOES.

YOU FORGOT TO *POLISH HIS BOOTS* AS HE CLIMBED UP!

THIS IS AWFUL!!

I'M SO SORRY!

THIS IS WHERE YOU LIVED?!

IT'S NOT A SAND CASTLE, BUT TO ME IT WAS HOME.

I'M SORRY, I DIDN'T MEAN IT THAT WAY.

NEVER MIND. WE HAVE TO FIND FERN.

FERN!

I'M GLAD YOU'RE ALIVE, KID!

IT'S THE *TOK!* DOING THIS, YOU KNOW. *IT'S WAR!*

I KNOW! WE SAW THEM ATTACK THE SAND CASTLE! THEY DESTROYED IT! *IT'S GONE!!*

GONE?! THE SAND CASTLE?

WE'D BETTER GET *OUT.* ALL YOUR PEOPLE ARE HEADING FOR THE HILLS. *YOU SHOULD JOIN THEM!*

WHAT ARE YOU READING?

A BOOK MY DAD USED TO READ TO ME. THESE *MIMIC* STORIES GAVE US *NIGHTMARES.*

WHERE ARE THEY, YOUR MOM AND DAD?

MY *DAD* GOT SICK FROM THE *CONTAMINATION.* WE HAD A *FARM* BACK THEN...

...BUT MY *MOM* COULDN'T MANAGE IT ON HER OWN, SO WE MOVED TO *CHRYSALIS.* THE *RED FEVER* TOOK HER.

I'M SO SORRY, *AN TZU!* I'VE KNOWN NOTHING BUT THE *SAND CASTLE.* I NEVER REALIZED THINGS WERE SO BAD OUTSIDE.

IT'S BEEN ROUGH LATELY, WITH THE *SHORTAGES.* WHAT ABOUT *YOUR* FAMILY?

DEAN PLUMB'S ADOPTION PROGRAM. MY SISTER, JESSA, MIGHT REMEMBER OUR REAL PARENTS, BUT I DON'T.

I REMEMBER MY DAD BEING ANGRY ABOUT THE STATE OF THE WORLDS.

THE ONLY WAY THE WORLDS CAN CHANGE IS IF THOSE BEACONS GET LIT.

WHAT MAKES YOU SO SURE ABOUT THAT?

I CAN FEEL IT. EVERYTHING AROUND US IS OUT OF BALANCE, NOT JUST PEOPLE...

BUT THE SAND CASTLE'S DESTROYED. MOST OF THE DANCERS GOT CAPTURED.

THAT'S WHY I HAVE TO GO TO MOON YATTA. JESSA IS THERE...

AND SHE'S THE ONLY HOPE FOR LIGHTING THE BEACON! I'M GOING TO CONVINCE HER TO COME BACK WITH ME TO CHRYSALIS.

IF SHE'S SO GOOD, WHAT'S SHE DOING ON MOON YATTA?

FROM WHAT I SAW IN THAT STADIUM, YOU SURE SEEM LIKE A GOOD SAND DANCER TO ME. CAN'T YOU LIGHT THE BEACONS?

YOU DON'T UNDERSTAND. IT'S NOT THAT SIMPLE.

Chapter 6
CAT ISLAND

THIS WAS ALWAYS ONE OF MY FAVORITES. *"THE QUEEN'S FINAL HOUR."*

READ IT TO ME?

Many epochs ago, the Great Queen and her court came to Mon Domani and its four moons.

With her came a brilliant Felid architect, who built the Five Beacons. His work dazzled the Queen, and she soon fell in love with him.

She called the Five Worlds her Garden of Souls. It was a magnificent success. Every breed of human thrived and lived in harmony. She and her architect had a son, who was named Prince Felid.

Then a great Catastrophe befell the Queen's Garden. The evil Mimic had snuck in, hidden within the Queen's court itself.... The Mimic's twisting, hateful influence spread like an illness.

Many fell under its sway.

The architect was one. The Queen's most trusted, beloved companion was seduced by the Mimic.

The Mimic rose in rebellion against the Great Queen. The Queen, Prince Felid, her court, and her faithful humans were surrounded atop Mount Chrysalis, on Mon Domani.

There the Mimic mounted a final assault, throwing his full might at her—and wounding her mortally.

But he underestimated her. The Great Queen shot one of her own arms right through the Mimic's core with such power, both arm and evil heart flew off Mon Domani!

Shooting across the worlds, they crashed into a desolate plain on Moon Toki. Deep, deep down they went, into the molten core of the blue world, sealing up in stone, where none might ever release the Mimic's heart.

She gave her dying breath to raise the Sand Castle, atop Mount Chrysalis, to be a sanctuary of training for humans to become ready...

...to one day defeat the Mimic, and reignite the great Beacons...

...or risk losing the Five Worlds altogether.

MOST *DEPRESSING* CHILDREN'S BOOK EVER WRITTEN, I KNOW.

THEY TAUGHT THE STORY DIFFERENTLY AT THE *SAND CASTLE*. DO YOU BELIEVE THE *MIMIC* REALLY EXISTS?

I DUNNO. I WAS *TERRIFIED* OF IT AS A KID. BUT NOBODY'S EVER SEEN IT, SO I'M NOT SO SURE.

UH-OH..

...TAKE COVER.

CH CHG CHG

PREPARE TO BE BOARDED!

UM, SIR, WE'RE JUST *PLANT PEOPLE* GOING ABOUT OUR BUSINESS. FIGHTS BETWEEN *HUMANS* ARE NONE OF OUR CONCERN.

STAND ASIDE! *MON DOMANI* IS NOW UNDER *TOKI* RULE. WE HAVE AUTHORITY TO INSPECT ALL CARGO BARGES TRAVELING BETWEEN CITY-STATES!

UNDER TOKI RULE?? BY ALL MEANS, COME ABOARD, CAPTAIN. DON'T MIND THE *PUFFERS* AND THE *IVY.* YOU'RE NOT *ALLERGIC,* ARE YOU?

UNLESS THE *YATTA CORPORATIONS* ARE INVOLVED IN SOME WAY.

BUT *WHY* STEAL *THE QUEEN'S BONES*? IT DOESN'T MAKE ANY SENSE!

THEY ARE TAKING OVER *THE WHOLE PLANET.* I EXPECT WHEN WE REACH *MAYAPOLIS*, IT WILL BE SWARMING WITH *TOKI* SOLDIERS....

WHAT'S WRONG, *AN TZU*? YOU LOOK LIKE YOU JUST SAW A GHOST.

A LITTLE *SEASICK* IS ALL.

WAS HE *REALLY* THAT GOOD?

THE *BEST*. BUT I DON'T THINK HE CAN EVER PLAY *STARBALL* AGAIN.

THAT'S SO SAD.

WHERE DID YOU LEARN THAT TUNE, LITTLE LAD? THAT'S VERY ANCIENT MUSIC!

I'M NOT SURE. I'VE BEEN HUMMING IT ALL MY LIFE.

LET ME TEACH YOU A TUNE WE PLANTS KNOW. PLAY IT WELL AND EVERY LAST ONE OF US WILL BE YOUR FRIEND.

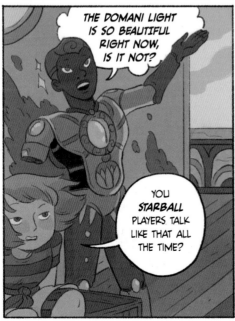

THE DOMANI LIGHT IS SO BEAUTIFUL RIGHT NOW, IS IT NOT?

YOU STARBALL PLAYERS TALK LIKE THAT ALL THE TIME?

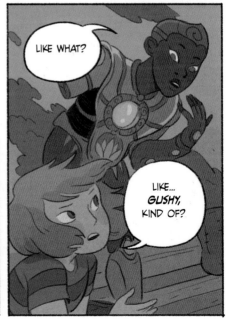

LIKE WHAT?

LIKE... GUSHY, KIND OF?

AM I...TOO *EMOTIONAL?*

UM, IT'S JUST KINDA *WEIRD.* BUT IT DOESN'T MATTTER.

NO, I *APPRECIATE* YOU TELLING ME. YOU'RE NOT *LIKE* OTHER *SAND DANCERS,* ARE YOU?

WHAT DO *YOU* KNOW ABOUT SAND DANCERS?

WHAT IF *YOU'RE THE ONE* WHO IS MEANT TO MAKE A *SAND WARRIOR?*

I'M NOT.

MY *UNCLE JEP* SAYS--

YOU DON'T GET IT!

MY *SISTER JESSA'S* THE ONE WHO CAN *SAND DANCE* FOR *REAL!* I'M GOING TO FIND HER, AND *SHE'S* GOING TO LIGHT THE BEACONS!

YOU CAN'T RUN FROM WHAT YOU REALLY ARE, *OONA.*

YOU ARE SO WEIRD!! I'M GOING TO SLEEP!

LOOK, I APPRECIATE WHAT YOU DID AT THE SAND CASTLE, BUT...

YOU *STARBALLERS* WERE HAVING YOUR *BIG GAME* RIGHT ON *BEACON DAY!* *LIKE IT WAS JUST SOME JOKE!*

SO DON'T TALK TO ME ABOUT "WHAT I REALLY AM"!

OPEN UP, HONEY. *FEEDING TIME.*

PUT YOUR HAND IN THE *GREEN* POOL, LITTLE HUMAN.

MY...HAND? BUT...*WHY*?

YOU *KNOW* WHY. I CAN'T PROMISE ANYTHING. BUT PERHAPS IT WILL HELP.

I KNOW YOU'RE THERE, *SAND DANCER GIRL.* YOU MIGHT AS WELL COME OUT.

PLSH

WOW.

OH LOOK!

PRINCE FELID ONCE STOOD HERE A LONG TIME AGO.

THOSE EYES...

WHAT.

NOTHING.

YOU HAVE THE **LIVING FIRE.**

PLANT PEOPLE ONCE CAME HERE TO COMMUNICATE WITH THE **GODS.**

YOU HAVE POWER.

YOU MAY NOT **WANT** IT...

BUT YOU **HAVE** IT.

I'M NO **SAND MASTER.** I...I CAN'T...I **CAN'T CONTROL THE SAND!**

WHY WOULD YOU WANT TO **CONTROL** IT? **IT KNOWS** WHAT'S NEEDED BETTER THAN YOU OR I.

YOU DON'T CONTROL IT. YOU LET IT CONTROL YOU.

THE PEOPLE WHO BUILT *THIS*--THE ONES WHO LEFT US THE *BEACONS*--THEY PUT THE WISDOM OF THE MOTHER WORLD *INTO THE SAND.*

WE PLANTS ARE DYING BECAUSE THE *FIVE WORLDS* ARE NOT AS THEY SHOULD BE.

THE MIMIC IS ROTTING THE QUEEN'S GARDEN.

THE ENEMY IS WINNING.

HUMANS ARE SO *CUT OFF*...

...THEY DON'T EVEN *FEEL* THEIR WORLD IS DYING AROUND THEM.

WE PLANTS AREN'T *SEPARATE*--WE CANNOT FEEL ISOLATED AS YOU DO.

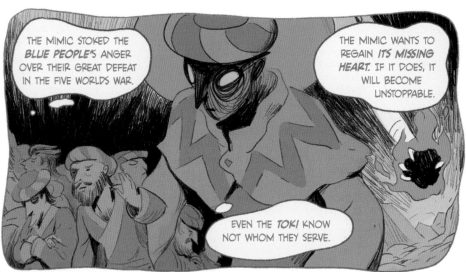

THE MIMIC STOKED THE *BLUE PEOPLE'S* ANGER OVER THEIR GREAT DEFEAT IN THE FIVE WORLDS WAR.

THE MIMIC WANTS TO REGAIN *ITS MISSING HEART.* IF IT DOES, IT WILL BECOME UNSTOPPABLE.

EVEN THE *TOKI* KNOW NOT WHOM THEY SERVE.

WHAT IS IT? WHAT DOES THE *MIMIC* LOOK LIKE?

IT COULD LOOK LIKE *ANYONE.* BUT THERE IS ONE THING IT CANNOT *IMITATE.*

THE LIVING FIRE.

FOR THE *MIMIC* IS A CREATURE OF *DESTRUCTION* ONLY.

OUR WORLDS WILL DIE UNLESS A SAND WARRIOR CAN RISE UP AND LIGHT THOSE BEACONS.

IF *ANYONE* CAN MAKE A *SAND WARRIOR*, IT'S *JESSA!* I'M GOING TO FIND HER AND TELL HER EVERYTHING, AND *SHE'LL* KNOW!

OONA. MAYBE *YOU* CAN DO IT.

THAT'S *RIDICULOUS.* I WAS THE *CLUMSIEST* SAND DANCER AT THE CASTLE.

AN EMBARRASSMENT.

WE ALL HAVE A JOB TO DO, *SAND DANCER GIRL.*

THE SAND LIVES. THE SAND KNOWS.

FOLLOW *ITS* GUIDANCE.

I'M NOT...

I WISH I COULD...

BUT...I'VE TRIED...

SO MANY TIMES...

LOOKS LIKE THAT SAND *KNEW...*

HOW TO *SMASH THINGS?*

THAT WAS UNFORTUNATE, SAND DANCER.

AN TZU, HELP ME WATER THE PLANTS OUTSIDE, WOULD YOU?

OONA, ARE YOU ALL RIGHT?

AN *TZU* SAID THERE WAS A PROBLEM ON THE ISLAND...

...BUT HE WOULDN'T SAY WHAT.

DON'T YOU HAVE *AUTOGRAPHS* TO SIGN OR SOMETHING?

LEAVE ME *ALONE!*

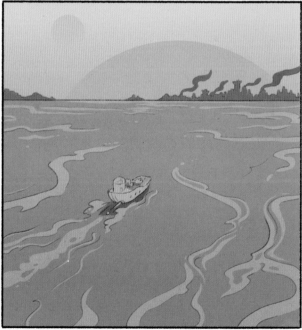

Chapter 7
THE SAND KNOWS

ON THE OTHER SIDE OF
MON DOMANI--TEMPORARY
TOKI HOLDING CAMP,
JUBINOO ARCHIPELAGO

WE GOT THE *TRAITOR SANDERSON*.... AND THE GREAT *DEAN PLUMB* ISN'T SO PROUD ANYMORE!

TAKE THEM TO THE BRIG, AND *DON'T* HARM THEM. ARE THE *QUEEN'S BONES* SECURE?

YES, COMMANDER *ZAYD.*

THEN LET US TAKE *THE SACRED RELIC* TO THE *FLYING FORTRESS ACADEMY!*

ZAYD!

YOUR HIGHNESS, MY SOVEREIGN, MY LIEGE!

YOU HAVE DONE *EXCELLENT* WORK, *ZAYD.*

YOU ARE *TOO KIND,* HIGHNESS! I AM ABOUT TO TAKE *THE QUEEN'S BONES* TO THE FLYING FORTRESS!

AH, YES. WELL, I'M *HERE,* AM I NOT? *I'LL TAKE OVER NOW.*

YOU HAVE IMPORTANT WORK TO DO *HERE ON MON DOMANI.* YOU NEED TO ROUND UP ALL THE REMAINING *SAND DANCERS,* DO YOU NOT?

BUT SURELY, MY PRINCE--

YES, YOUR HIGHNESS, BUT *OUR OFFICERS* CAN--

WONDERFUL WORK, *ZAYD.* WE WILL NOT FORGET IT.

156

PORT MAYAPOLIS

I'LL BE BACK SHORTLY.

WITH JESSA.

WAIT, *OONA*, THIS CAN'T BE RIGHT.

YOU DON'T EVEN KNOW YOUR SISTER WILL *LISTEN* TO YOU!

AND *YOU'RE* THE ONE WHO DID THAT *SAND-FORM THING* IN THE STADIUM, NOT HER!

DIDN'T YOU *SEE* WHAT HAPPENED IN *MEADOW'S* SANCTUARY? YOU THINK I CAN LIGHT *ANYTHING?!?*

ALL MY *ANIFORMS* DO IS MAKE A *MESS.* IF *ANYONE* CAN LIGHT A *BEACON--*

MY UNCLE JEP STUDIED THE *BEACONS* FOR YEARS. *NOBODY* KNOWS MORE ABOUT THEM THAN HE DOES.

BYE, *AN TZU.* BYE, *JAX.*

AH, *MISS LEE.* WELCOME ABOARD THE *MOON MOTH.*

I NEED *YOU TWO* TO STEP ASIDE, OVER HERE.

YES, I'M RETURNING TO FAMILY ON *MOON YATTA* TOO.

THE *TOKI* SERVANTS ALL RAN OFF. I *HAVE* NO CHOICE.

ROTTEN *BLUE-SKINS!* WE DIDN'T EVEN PUT UP A *PROPER* FIGHT!! THEY STOLE THE *QUEEN'S BONES!!*

I DIDN'T LIKE 'EM *HIGH-AND-MIGHTY SAND DANCERS,* BUT THEM *BONES* WAS *OURS!!*

161

SOME *SAO SABLO* STREET URCHIN, AND...THE *STARBALL* PLAYER *JAX AMBOY!*

JAX AMBOY?

"THE *NATURAL BOY*"?!

I SAW HIM PLAY THE *TOURMALINES* BACK IN--

HEH!

WHAT?!

SLAM!

WHY WEREN'T THEY ARRESTED AT ONCE?!

WELL, YOUR INSTRUCTIONS WERE--

SILENCE! PUT THE WORD OUT NOW! FIND THEM!

FIND HER!

THE WAY IS CLEAR.

THE *TOKI* CONTROL THE *POLICE BOTS!* GOOD THING THEY'RE SO SLOW AND CLUNKY...

BRR–ING!

BRRR–ING!!

GO AWAY!!

UNCLE JEP! IT'S ME, *JAX!*

PALULUAN PILES! IS *STOAK* WITH YOU?

NO, *UNCLE JEP.*

168

I'M GLAD YOU MADE IT OUT OF THE STADIUM.

DOES *DERRICK STOAK* KNOW HIS STAR *LEATHERHEAD* IS WANDERING AROUND UNSUPERVISED?

NO, *UNCLE JEP.*

AND YOU BROUGHT *COMPANY.*

THESE ARE MY *FRIENDS*, UNCLE JEP.

YOU'RE WELCOME TO HANG OUT UNTIL *STOAK* COMES TO TAKE YOU AWAY AGAIN.

...ALL THE CAPTIVES FROM THE *SAND CASTLE* ARE BEING TAKEN TO *TOKI*, DID YOU KNOW?

BE MY GUESTS AND ENJOY ALL THIS TERRIFIC *NEWS*...

VEA... VECTOR...

TELL ME, *JAX*, HOW *WERE* YOU ABLE TO GET AWAY FROM YOUR TEAM? DIDN'T THEY HAVE YOU ON *A PRETTY TIGHT LEASH*?

MY ARM WAS CRUSHED.

WELL, *THAT* WAS FORTUNATE.

WHAT'S *WRONG* WITH THIS GUY?

170

YOUR *UNCLE JEP* IS WORSE THAN THE *TOKI!*

"UNCLE JEP," THAT'S ME. GOOD OL' *UNCA JEPPY.*

YOU MANAGED TO *KEEP IT UP,* MY GOOD BOY.

THEY DON'T EVEN *KNOW.*

WOULDN'T *DERRICK STOAK* BE PROUD!

DON'T EVEN KNOW WHAT...? *KEEP WHAT UP?*

WHY, MY *FIRST* CONTRIBUTION TO THE GOOD OF HUMANKIND!

SIT DOWN, MY BOY.

I'VE MISSED YOU. EVER SINCE *HE TOOK YOU AWAY* FROM ME.

THIS *"NATURAL BOY"*...

...IS THE LAST OF THE LINE OF *SENTIENT MODELS J.A.X. 3201.*

BUT HE CAN'T BE... THE...*THE ANDROID LAW--*

OH YES, THE *LAW.* NOT A BAD LAW, I SUPPOSE. FOR THOSE WHO AREN'T *ABOVE* LAWS. WHEN YOU'RE *DERRICK STOAK,* CO-FOUNDER OF *NANOTEX* CORPORATION, THEY'RE *OPTIONAL,* OF COURSE.

IT CAN'T BE... *NOT JAX!*

NOT JAX AMBOY!

SO YOU WERE A *FAN?* CAN'T BLAME YOU. MY HANDIWORK REALLY WAS *TOP-NOTCH* ON THIS ONE....

WHEN THE *ANDROID HUMANOID APPEARANCE LAWS* WERE PASSED, ALL MY BEAUTIFUL *JAX* MODELS HAD TO BE *DESTROYED!*

BUT MY EMPLOYERS SECRETLY KEPT *ONE* MODEL--AND USED HIM FOR THEIR CURSED *STARBALL* TEAM.

I THINK I'M GONNA BE *SICK.*

WELL, **THAT** EXPLAINS A LOT. TRYING **A LITTLE TOO HARD** TO BE A REAL PERSON. **"YOU CAN'T RUN FROM WHAT YOU REALLY ARE."** THANKS FOR THE **ADVICE!**

HMPH!

AND I GUESS WE CAN **FORGET** EVERYTHING THAT ANDROID SAID, RIGHT? LIKE THE PART ABOUT YOU BEING AN EXPERT ON THE **BEACONS?**

WHY ARE **YOU** CONCERNED WITH THE **BEACONS?**

BECAUSE OONA IS GOING TO LIGHT ONE!

WHAT DID YOU SAY?

IT'S TRUE. I'M GOING TO **CHRYSALIS**...TO LIGHT THE **BEACON.**

OR DIE TRYING.

FWOOOF

THE LIVING FIRE!

THE MARK OF THE SAND WARRIOR!

THE *BEACONS!* I STUDIED THEM FOR YEARS. IT WAS MY *OBSESSION!*

THE *SCIENTIST* IN ME JUST HAD TO UNDERSTAND THIS GIANT *MYSTERY* STARING DOWN AT US.

BUT *WHAT* DO THE *BEACONS* REALLY DO?!

IT'S AN *ASTONISHING* DESIGN. WHOEVER THOSE *FELID GODS* WERE, THEY CLEARLY KNEW ABOUT TURNING *MOONS* INTO *PLANETS* AND *PLANETS* INTO *SUNS!*

THE BEACONS WERE MEANT TO *SPEED UP* OR *SLOW DOWN* THE GROWTH OF *ENTIRE WORLDS!* CAN YOU *IMAGINE?* ONLY THEY'VE BEEN *OFF* FOR FAR TOO LONG!

BUT *WHY?*

SO MANY *GREAT SAND DANCERS* HAVE *TRIED* TO LIGHT THEM.

MAYBE THOSE SAND DANCERS WERE MISSING THE *REAL KEY.*

THE LIVING FIRE.

THAT'S WHAT'S GOING TO LIGHT THE *BEACON*, ISN'T IT?

YES! THE *OVERHEATING* OF THE FIVE WORLDS CAN BE REVERSED *AT LAST!*

BUT OUR *FIVE DAYS* ARE ALMOST OVER!

YOU'RE GOING TO NEED HELP. LET'S GO TO MY LAB.

Chapter 9

ALTERATIONS

MAYAPOLIS CENTER,
NANOTEX LABS

THE **SAME** SAND THAT THE **TOKI** ARE USING FOR THEIR **SAND SHADOWS?**

I'M AFRAID SO. MY RESEARCH ON **TOKI** WAS FOR **MEDICAL PURPOSES**, BUT IT'S BEEN **WEAPONIZED**. HOW COULD I NOT HAVE SEEN **THAT** COMING?

THAT'S WHY DARK SAND CAN **EXPLODE!**

YES. UNLIKE THE **WHITE SAND** FROM **MON DOMANI**, THE **DARK SAND** YOU FIND INSIDE **MOON TOKI** IS **VOLATILE.**

IT CAN BE MADE TO BLOW UP.

SNIP~

OF COURSE THAT GOT MY **EMPLOYERS** INTERESTED!

THEY MUST HAVE MADE A **DEAL** WITH THE **TOKI** RULERS AND **SOLD** IT TO THEM.

THNK

DARK SAND MIXED WITH MY LITTLE **NANOBOTS**--AND LOOK AT US NOW...**A CONQUERED WORLD!**

BUT LET'S GIVE THEM **A TASTE OF THEIR OWN MEDICINE!**

UH... WHAT ARE YOU DOING?

ZZZZT

WE WON'T NEED MORE THAN A *PINCH* OF THIS TO POWER *YOUR NEW ARM....*

JAX, MY BOY, YOU'RE GOING TO NEED TO *PRACTICE* CAREFULLY WITH THIS!

SLIP

START WITH ONE FINGER AT A TIME! *AWAY FROM EVERYBODY!*

ZZT!

?

K-K

UNCLE *JEP*, WHAT WILL I DO WITHOUT *STARBALL?*

ZZRT!!

WELL, THAT'S SOMETHING YOU'LL HAVE TO FIGURE OUT, *KIDDO...LIKE THE REST OF US.*

BUT I'M NOT A REAL BOY.

BUT IT SEEMS YOU HAVE *REAL FRIENDS.* YOU CAN START BY HELPING *THEM, JAX.*

YOUR NEW ARM WILL GIVE YOU A LITTLE *EDGE.*

WELL, I *AM A* REAL BOY!

A REAL *DISAPPOINTED* BOY!!

THUNK

FFFFF

UNKNOWN GENETIC PROFILE.

BEEP

BOOP

BLIP

HOLD ON A MINUTE...

WHAT'S THIS *CHROMOSOMIC WORK* HERE? WHERE DID YOU GET *THIS* DONE?!

WHAT ARE YOU TALKING ABOUT?

THIS *STUFF*... WHAT IS IT? THESE AREN'T EVEN *AMINO-GRAFTS!* SOMETHING ELSE.

I HAVE *NO IDEA* WHAT YOU'RE EVEN SAYING.

YOU'VE HAD *MASSIVE GENETIC ALTERATIONS.* A *BILLION* NANOS ARE DOING...*SOMETHING* IN YOU!! *WHAT IS GOING ON HERE?!*

WAIT, WAIT, WAIT... I HAVEN'T SEEN THIS LEVEL OF *TRANSFORMATION* SINCE...SINCE...

...SINCE THE DISASTER AT ATBAL-BALAK!

WHAT? WHERE?

THE CEILING, JAX! BLAST THE CEILING!!

CRAK

THNK

I'VE RUN OUT OF POWER....

ARGH! *RECHARGING TIME!* THIS WON'T HOLD THEM OFF LONG....

THERE'S AN EXIT THAT WAY. *FOLLOW ME!*

H-HNG...

AH—

BUT YOU...

YOU HAVE BROUGHT ME *HOPE.*

MORE HOPE THAN I'VE HAD IN A VERY LONG TIME... *GO, SON.*

HELP *OONA LEE.*

IS THAT MY NEW *CORE DIRECTIVE?*

NO. IT'S THE RIGHT THING TO DO.

THE *HUMAN* THING TO DO.

KA BOOOM!!

YOU INCOMPETENT FOOLS! YOUR INSTRUCTIONS WERE TO CAPTURE THEM UNHARMED!

WE ARE ALMOST SURE THEY ESCAPED *BEFORE* THE EXPLOSION....

SLAM

SHE FOUND HER WAY TO *PROFESSOR ETTO'S LAB.* WHERE TO *NOW?*

I CAN DO NO MORE FOR HER.

THE *DARK SAND* IS POISONING HER IN A WAY I CAN'T SEEM TO STOP. THIS IS BEYOND MY POWERS. *WE'RE LOSING HER.*

OONA! WE NEED YOU!

I'M SORRY....

CAN'T WE *CUT OUT* THE DARK SAND FROM HER SHOULDER?

WHOA, WHOA, *WHOA!* SHE'S A *LIVING* PERSON, REMEMBER?!

THE *DARK SAND* IS SPREADING IN HER. IT HAS A LIFE OF ITS OWN.

THE SAND LIVES...

THE SAND KNOWS...

STRANGE SANDSTONE. IT CONTAINS *FOUR* DIFFERENT SANDS.

SAND LIVES... SAND KNOWS...

SO WHAT?!

OONA IS DYING!!! DON'T YOU GET IT?!

WHITE SAND OF **MON DOMANI...**

RED SAND OF **MOON YATTA...** GOLDEN SAND OF **SALASSANDRA...**

EMERALD SAND OF **GRIMBO (E)...**

I'M ONLY MISSING ONE...!!

HF HFF...

SPLASH

THE MISSING SAND IS... *THE DARK SAND OF TOKI!*

WHICH IS *IN YOU...*

THE SAND WARRIOR!

THE PROPHECIES!

THE BEACON! I NEED TO GO TO CHRYSALIS! ARE YOU GUYS COMING?!

I AM COMING.

BUT HOW?

JAX, YOU COULD PILOT ONE OF THOSE *SHOEBOXES*, RIGHT?

PROBABLY, YES, BUT WE CAN'T JUST *BORROW*--

I BET MY SAND WARRIOR CAN!

WHO'S BOTTOM OF THE CLASS NOW? I'LL SHOW THEM WHAT THE *CLUMSY SAND DANCER* CAN DO!

JUMP

LOOK AT THAT. THE SUNS MAKE A PERFECT LINE!

WE HAVE MAYBE AN HOUR BEFORE OUR TIME IS UP.

STEP ON IT, ROBOT BOY!

WE'RE GOING FULL SPEED.... ACTUALLY, I *MIGHT* BE ABLE TO HELP.

SOMEONE TAKE THE WHEEL.

COMMANDER ZAYD! A GIANT SAND ANIFORM WAS SEEN IN MAYAPOLIS. IT GOT AWAY, AND THE SAND DANCER AND HER ASSOCIATES COMMANDEERED A HATBOX.

IT'S HEADING FOR CHRYSALIS. DO WE TAKE THEM DOWN?

HOLD YOUR FIRE!

TURN AROUND! TAKE US BACK TO CHRYSALIS!

TO THE PORT, COMMANDER?

NO. TO THE WHITE BEACON.

THAT'S WHERE YOU'LL MEET ME. SEE THE PIERS? DROP ME OFF ON THIS SIDE, HERE.

OONA, DO YOU *KNOW* WHAT YOU'RE DOING NOW?

THE SAND...

...KNOWS.

YOUR HIGHNESS? ARE THE *QUEEN'S BONES* IN THE *FLYING FORTRESS*?

PLANS CHANGE, *ZAYD.*

LEAVE THE *RELIC* TO ME.

WHAT OF THE *SAND DANCER*?

I WILL HAVE HER SOON.

SHE IS CLEARLY HEADING FOR THE *BEACON.* YOU KNOW WHAT THIS COULD MEAN. *NOW COMES THE TEST OF YOUR LOYALTY.*

IF SHE GETS THERE, *SHE MUST DIE.* IS THAT CLEAR?

YES, CROWN PRINCE.

THIS IS YOUR LAST CHANCE FOR A PEACEFUL SURRENDER!

AH!!

LOOK!

GASP!

OKAY, *BOT BOY,* LET ME OFF THERE!

COULD YOU STOP CALLING ME THAT?

HUH. NOT PROGRAMMED FOR *COMEBACKS,* I GUESS.

IT'S WORKING! WHATEVER YOU'RE DOING DOWN THERE, IT'S SLOWING THEM DOWN!

I NEED TO REACH THE TOP, JAX!

SHE...

LIT...THE *LIVING FIRE?!*

SEND IN *THE SAND SHADOWS,* COMMANDER?

YES.

DOOM

DOOM

OONA!! SAND SHADOWS!!!

I SEE THEM.

I CAN'T STOP THEM!!

219

THE *SAND DANCER* GIRL DID IT. *SHE LIT THE BEACON.*

JESSA ZAYD! YOU HAVE BEEN SUMMONED BY THE PRINCE TO APPEAR BEFORE *THE COBALT COUNCIL.*

THIS WORLD HOPPER IS THE *FLITORI*, FIRST STOP *SALASSANDRA.*

IT BELONGS TO THE THREE *MAD CAPTAINS*--THERE ARE SOME *WEIRD RUMORS* ABOUT THEM, BUT THEY'RE NOT WITH *THE TOKI.*

AREN'T YOU COMING WITH US, *FERN?*

MY WORK IS *HERE.* YOUR WORK IS *OUT THERE.*

HOPE YOU CAN FIND TREATMENT WHEREVER YOU END UP.

PLEASE, TAKE OFF, TAKE OFF, TAKE OFF... *OH NO!!*

HOLD THAT SHIP!

YOU! HAVE YOU SEEN TWO KIDS AND A STARBALL PLAYER?

I HAVE! I MOST CERTAINLY HAVE! I'VE ALWAYS BEEN A BIG *LEATHERHEADS* FAN, AND YOU WOULDN'T BELIEVE--

WE HAVE A WITNESS!

WHERE WERE THEY?

JAX AMBOY! I'M SURE IT WAS HIM!!

ALL I WAS ASKING FOR WAS *ONE QUICK AUTOGRAPH,* BUT *NO!* YOU KNOW HOW THESE CELEBRITIES--

WHERE?! HOW LONG AGO?

OH, TEN MINUTES AGO, OVER AT **MOUSERIDERS DOCK.**

HE WAS BOARDING THE **RIVERMAIDEN**...WHICH **I THOUGHT** WAS KIND OF ODD FOR SOMEONE AS RICH--

MOUSERIDERS DOCK! ON THE DOUBLE!!

UNCLE JEP, DO YOU STILL EXIST WITHOUT YOUR BODY?

WHAT HAPPENS TO HUMANS WHEN THEY DIE?

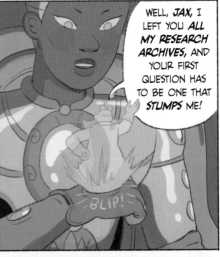

WELL, **JAX,** I LEFT YOU **ALL MY RESEARCH ARCHIVES,** AND YOUR FIRST QUESTION HAS TO BE ONE THAT **STUMPS** ME!

IT'S FOR YOU TO FIGURE OUT, **KIDDO!**

AND HEY, NO MATTER WHAT COMES, I HELPED *THE SAND WARRIOR* LIGHT *THE FIRST BEACON.*

ON TO *SALASSANDRA!*

I DON'T THINK WE WANT TO GET OFF AT *SALASSANDRA* NEXT.

WAIT, YOU'RE NOT *STILL* GOING TO LOOK FOR YOUR SISTER, ARE YOU? *YOU'RE CLEARLY THE ONE!*

NO, I *FOUND* MY SISTER.

JESSA...WAS THE *DARK-SAND DANCER* CONTROLLING THAT GIANT SHADOW AT THE *BEACON.* SHE...*BECAME A TOKI.* SOMEHOW.

WHAT?! IS THAT EVEN POSSIBLE?!

I DON'T KNOW *HOW.* BUT YES. *THE MIMIC IS BEHIND ALL OF THIS.* IF YOUR BOOK IS RIGHT, *AN TZU,* THE TOKI WANT TO FREE THE MIMIC'S HEART!

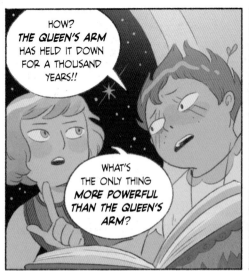

HOW? **THE QUEEN'S ARM** HAS HELD IT DOWN FOR A THOUSAND YEARS!!

WHAT'S THE ONLY THING **MORE POWERFUL THAN THE QUEEN'S ARM**?

...**THE REST OF THE QUEEN'S BONES!!**

THAT'S WHY THE **TOKI** STOLE THEM!

BUT THERE ARE SO MANY THINGS I STILL DON'T UNDERSTAND...LIKE WHY **PROFESSOR ETTO** TOLD ME I HAD BEEN **GENETICALLY ALTERED.**

AND WHAT DID HE MEAN ABOUT FINDING ANSWERS AT "**ATBAL-BALAK**"? **WHERE IS THAT?**

I THINK I CAN HELP WITH THAT ONE.

YEAH, HE SORTA SLEEPS.

JAX! YOU'RE UP! OR... DO YOU EVEN SLEEP?

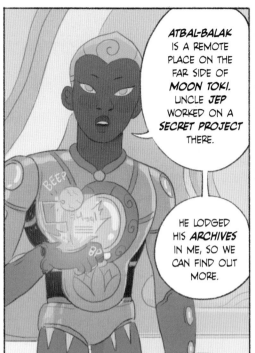

ATBAL-BALAK IS A REMOTE PLACE ON THE FAR SIDE OF **MOON TOKI**. UNCLE **JEP** WORKED ON A **SECRET PROJECT** THERE.

HE LODGED HIS **ARCHIVES** IN ME, SO WE CAN FIND OUT MORE.

BUT WHAT DOES THAT HAVE TO DO WITH ME?

LET'S ASK UNCLE JEP!

UNCLE, WHAT IS THE CONNECTION BETWEEN **OONA** AND **ATBAL-BALAK**?

...

TRANSLATION, PLEASE.

OOPS. **ENCRYPTED.** I'LL HAVE TO WORK ON THAT.

I'M **STARVING.** LET'S GO OVER TO THE MESS HALL....

I TOLD YOU THERE WAS SOMETHING ABOUT THOSE THREE.

IT APPEARS WE HAVE *THE CHOSEN ONE* ON BOARD.

WHAT SHALL WE DO ABOUT THAT?

END OF BOOK 1:
THE SAND WARRIOR

To Julien and Clio—MS

To Shudan, Felix, and Elia—AS

To Mom and Pop—XB

To my friends and family—MR

To all my friends—BS

ACKNOWLEDGMENTS

Tanya McKinnon,
for support high and low, above and beyond

Our amazing Random House team:
Michelle Nagler, Chelsea Eberly, Elizabeth Tardiff, Kelly McGauley, Kim Lauber, Alison Kolani,
Dominique Cimina, Aisha Cloud, Lisa Nadel, Adrienne Waintraub, Laura Antonacci, John Adamo,
Joe English, Jocelyn Lange, Mallory Loehr, Barbara Marcus

+ Special thanks for added help, friendship & magic:
Siena Siegel, Sonia Siegel, Macarena Mata, Julie Sandfort, Gene Luen Yang,
Lee Wade, Sam Bosma, Kali Ciesemier, Noelle Stevenson, Carter Goodrich,
Moebius, Ursula K. LeGuin, Doris Lessing, Lois McMaster Bujold

ISBN 978-1-338-31573-8

12 11 10 9 8 7 6 5 4 3 2 1   18 19 20 21 22 23

Printed in Heshan, China   62

First Scholastic printing, September 2018

MARK SIEGEL has written and illustrated several award-winning picture books and graphic novels, including the *New York Times* bestseller **Sailor Twain, or the Mermaid in the Hudson.** He is also the founder and editorial director of First Second Books at Macmillan. He lives with his family in New York.

ALEXIS SIEGEL is a writer and translator based in London, England. He has translated a number of bestselling graphic novels, including Joann Sfar's **The Rabbi's Cat** and Pénélope Bagieu's **Exquisite Corpse** into English and Gene Luen Yang's **American Born Chinese** into French.

XANTHE BOUMA is an illustrator based in Southern California. When not working on picture books, fashion illustration, and comics, Xanthe enjoys soaking up the beachside sun.

MATT ROCKEFELLER is an illustrator and comic book artist from Tucson, Arizona. His work has appeared in a variety of formats, including book covers, picture books, and animation. Matt lives in New York City.

BOYA SUN is an illustrator and coauthor of the upcoming graphic novel **Chasma Knights.** Originally from China, Boya has traveled from Canada to the United States and now resides in the charming city of Baltimore.